ARE YOU SMARTER THAN A 5TH GRADER?

TEST YOUR SMARTS!

Scrapbook

by Lisa L. Ryan-Herndon

Thanks to Mark Burnett Productions,
especially Mark Burnett, Roy Bank,
Barry Poznick, John Stevens, Sue Guercioni,
Amanda Harrell, and Laura Ambriz

SCHOLASTIC INC.
New York Toronto London Auckland Sydney
Mexico City New Delhi Hong Kong Buenos Aires

The publisher would like to thank the following for their kind permission to use their photographs in this book:

Are You Smarter Than a 5th Grader? photos courtesy of JMBP, INC.; 11 Marki Ann Meyer © Fox; 14 Paint Tray © Viktoriia Kulish/iStockphoto; 14 – 21 Guitar, Paint Tubes, Elephant, Polar Bear, Continents Map, Quill Pen, Teeth, Note Art courtesy of Shutterstock.com; 22 March Calendar © Sean Locke/iStockphoto; 22 – 34 American Flag, Piggybank, Geotool, Clouds, Dog Sled Team, Pencil, Calculator, Dinosaur, Periodic Table, Hieroglyph, Sistine Chapel courtesy of Shutterstock.com; 34 Nobel Peace Prize Medal ©Topham/The Image Works; 35 Compass on Map and Globe courtesy of Shutterstock.com; 38 Mars Earth Comparison © Exclusive to iStockphoto; 38 – 39 Solar System, Algebra Blackboard, Mathematic Equation courtesy of Shutterstock.com; 40 Lewis and Clark map courtesy of NOAA's National Geodetic Survey; 40 – 41 Mount Rushmore and Pen and Ink courtesy of Shutterstock.com.

Published by Scholastic Inc. SCHOLASTIC and associated logos are trademarks and/or registered trademarks of Scholastic Inc.

ISBN-13: 978-0-545-04684-8
ISBN-10: 0-545-04684-X

Designed by Michelle Martinez Design, Inc.
Photo researched by Michelle Martinez and Els Rijper

12 11 10 9 8 7 6 5 4 3 2 1   8 9 10 11/0

Printed in the U.S.A.
First printing, February 2008

CLASS IS IN SESSION

How many of school's golden rules do you remember? Since its network debut on February 27, 2007, *Are You Smarter Than a 5th Grader?* has proven to more than 26 million television viewers that most adults *did* forget their grade-school lessons. Of the first 49 contestants, only six passed all five levels, with zero winning a million dollars, and every contestant admitting they were *not* smarter than a 10-year-old in the fifth grade! Turn the page for behind-the-scenes stories, snapshot show moments, and a chance to learn if you would ace the same quiz.

TEACHERS' LOUNGE

Stories from the Set

When a new series is created by Emmy®-winning television producer Mark Burnett (*Survivor*, *The Apprentice*) and his production team, audiences expect to see regular people using their skills to overcome tough situations. The school classroom has proven to be one of the roughest environments for contestants! Here's an exclusive peek at the making of the hit game show courtesy of its executive producers.

The set

Q. What's it like working behind-the-scenes on *Are You Smarter Than a 5th Grader?*

A. The office that houses our staff is always bustling with activity. Staff members bring in their dogs to play and frolic with the crew. Our kitchen is stocked with goodies and the occasional cake for someone's birthday. People are watching contestant videos, music can be heard, and staffers are brainstorming about possible show ideas. Everyone is very busy trying to make each show great.

Q. How do you come up with those brain-melting questions?

A. The writers and research team study grade-school textbooks, read teacher study guides and encyclopedias, and many other sources. Sometimes they spend time with the producers, quizzing them on their knowledge. Occasionally, they will present the staff with brainteasers like the following: The human body has 10 body parts that are three letters long. Can you name them? (Answer: arm, leg, eye, ear, toe, lip, hip, jaw, rib, and gum.)

Q. How do you pick the kids and the contestants for the show?

A. To get the word out, the Casting Department will put postings on the Internet, put up flyers in stores, and even ask people while they're out shopping or eating if they want to be on the show. Sometimes people hear about the auditions from their friends, or call the office to find out if they can be on the show. When the Casting Department meets people they think may be good contestants, they invite them to come in and audition.

Q. Tell us some stories from the set.

A. One woman brought her son in to audition, [but he wasn't old enough yet]. The casting director noticed that the mom was very personable, animated, and likeable. He talked her into auditioning. All the producers loved her, and they picked her to be on the show right away. Susan Garguilo won $25,000!

Contestant Dennis Furden came up with the idea that it would be fun to present Jeff with a shiny red apple. But the only apple he could find was the smallest green apple he'd ever seen. Just as Dennis was going on, a production assistant came running over with a big, beautiful, shiny red apple in his hand — and Dennis dropped it! The producer grabbed the apple from the floor, threw it to Dennis, and Dennis ran onstage. "Dennis," says Jeff, "you brought me an apple with a bite in it!"

We all had our special handshake called "blowin' up." This is where we would lightly knock knuckles and then open our hands up like a firework. It was our way of telling each other, "You're doing great!"

Setting the Stage

Q. **Describe one day of taping an episode.**

A. A typical show day starts very early — sometimes before 6 AM.! While the kids are in school with their tutor, the contestants arrive. They practice playing the game with the producers. We want to make sure that they are familiar with the rules of the game and comfortable under pressure. Once contestants get on stage with all the lights and the cheering, and meeting Jeff for the first time, it can be very nerve-wracking, even scary! So we try and make them feel at ease and let them know exactly what to expect — except for the questions and answers!

After they practice the game, the contestants are taken to the wardrobe room, where the wardrobe stylist decides which clothes they will wear. Then the hair stylist and makeup artist fix up their hair and put them in makeup — even the guys! Everyone wants to look their best on TV in front of millions of people!

After that, they meet the stage manager. It's the stage manager's job to make sure the contestants are in the right place at the right time. The stage manager leads them to the soundstage where the set is located. The soundstage is a very big building about five stories high and as big as many schools. It holds the set, cameras, dozens of crew people who run the show, and hundreds of audience members. The stage manager leads them behind the set to the place where they enter the stage. They practice their entrance down the hallway into the classroom,

TRUE OR FALSE?
IN THE EARTH'S WATER CYCLE,
PRECIPITATION TYPICALLY
FOLLOWS CONDENSATION.

$1,000,000

On stage

The long hallway

standing behind the podium, and locking in their answers by hitting the button. It's not as easy as it looks!

After that, the contestants wait [in their dressing rooms] until it's their turn to play the game. The stage manager leads them to the back of the stage [and they wait for their cue]. When Jeff says, "Are you ready to meet our new student, kids?" they run onto the stage and find out if they're smarter than a 5th grader!

Q. What skills do you need to become a TV producer or writer?

A. There are lots of different jobs on a TV show, from technical ones such as camera operator, to creative ones such as set designer. The writers come from many different back-grounds, but all of them spent a lot of time in school. If you want to be a writer, stay in school to learn about the world around you — and then write about it.

The producers also come from different backgrounds, but they have all worked in television for many years. They help the casting people choose the contestants and the kids, and then they spend a lot of time getting to know the contestants, finding out what makes them interesting, what their families are like, and even what they'd like to do with a million dollars!

The most important thing a producer does is make the contestant feel at home. If the contestant goes on the stage and has a great time, and Jeff and the audience have a great time too, then the producer has done his or her job well. If you'd like to be a TV producer, or even a host, it's easy to make your own shows with a video camera and your friends — you can even use a cell phone. Put your shows on web sites and see how popular they are. Good luck!

HEAD OF THE CLASS

Jeff Foxworthy

Executive Producer Barry Poznick remembers how comedian-actor-writer Jeff Foxworthy became our favorite teacher in this TV classroom.

"Jeff never thought he would become the host of a game show. But when he heard about *5th Grader*, he liked the idea right away. Jeff has two daughters of his own and knew immediately the show had great family appeal. So he flew out to Los Angeles to meet the executive producers, Mark Burnett, Roy Bank, John Stevens, and [me], and hosted a practice show…to make sure this concept would be the right fit for him. He loved it! And the network loved him . . . a deal was done instantly, and he started hosting the show less than a week later."

Jeff takes a seat.

Jeff's best subject is probably U.S. Geography because he travels a lot! Jeff and his family live in his hometown of Atlanta, Georgia, and he commutes to Los Angeles, California, for the show. Jeff hosts two shows in one day. Very early on the day of taping, Jeff meets with producers about that day's contestants. He goes through hair, makeup, and wardrobe before lunch. Prior to filming, Jeff goes out on stage and chats with the audience, just like in his stand-up days.

What's our favorite teacher's background? Jeffrey M. "Jeff" Foxworthy graduated from Hapeville High School and attended Georgia Tech University. In 1984, his friends encouraged him to compete in "The Great Southeastern Laugh Off" at The Punchline Comedy Club. Jeff won, and began an extraordinarily successful entertainment career. He is the largest selling comedy-recording artist in history, a multiple Grammy Award nominee, and best-selling author of more than 22 books. He launched *The Blue Collar Comedy Tour* franchise, which resulted in three movies, a TV show, and concert tour. Jeff's natural comedic timing and down-home manner charms audiences of all ages and backgrounds. How does he handle it? With an easy-going chuckle and a punch line.

MEET THE CLASS

The freshman class of the series had an awesome after-school job — TV star! These six real-life fifth graders were a mix of personalities, skills, interests, and backgrounds. Jacob and Alana had been on a TV program a few years ago, while Laura graduated mid-season to another show. Marki, a student new to answering questions in front of a camera, took over Laura's desk. Kyle and Spencer were also new to TV filming. Everyone made the new kid, Marki, feel right at home on and off the set.

Late for school? Not these kids!

SPENCER   MARKI   ALANA   KYLE   JACOB

Our smarty-pants fifth graders are psyched for class to begin.

Laura Marano

Best subject: Science and Social Studies

♥ ♥ ♥

Matching Up Her Pals

Kyle Collier

Best subject: Math, Reading, and History

♥ ♥ ♥

Karate, Flying, and His Horse Bill Williams

Spencer Martin

Best subject: Science

♥ ♥ ♥

Pogo-Stick Jumping and Skateboarding

Alana Etheridge

Best subject: Math

♥ ♥ ♥

Singing Hip-Hop

Jacob Hays

Best subject: History, Science, and Math

♥ ♥ ♥

Magic, Girls, and *Good* Pizza

Marki Ann Meyer

Best subject: Math

♥ ♥ ♥

Tackle Trampoline Football with Her 5 Brothers and 3 Sisters

SMARTS TEST

Cramming for the Quiz

Have you studied for the test? Just like on the show, you can now take the same quiz along with the class. Scout for help with student cheats and hints in the show's flashbacks. You can then check your answers at the end of each grade to learn if you passed or failed in your quest to prove that you *are* smarter than a fifth grader. Go grab a pencil and a piece of paper!

Welcome to the class!

1ST GRADE

- ★ Art
- ★ Music
- ★ Animal Science
- ★ World Geography

Pick a student!

LAURA

These grown-ups are excited about going back to school. They run, shout, bike, jump, and roller skate down the set's hallway — detention behavior at a real school — ready to take that quiz and win some major lunch money. Once at their desk, they learn it isn't so elementary. Ask Michael Warren or rocket scientist Karl Schab. They flunked out on first-grade questions. How will you do?

Your new classmate!

Michael Warren

ART

Q. Pick out the primary colors from this paint box.

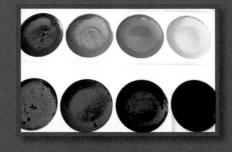

Q. Secondary colors are made by mixing two primary colors. What are the combinations for making the three secondary colors?

MUSIC

Q. The guitar is a string instrument. Name two other string instruments.

Q. A string instrument makes music when its strings are plucked. How does a percussion instrument make music?

Brain Bubble

Paint Chips

Contestant Adam Adore almost flunked out because he thought art was an easy subject. Classmate Kyle saved Adam after he mixed up his primary and secondary colors. Adam made it through the fourth grade with $175,000 before dropping out.

☺ Make an **intermediate** or **tertiary** color by mixing **primary** and **secondary** colors.

☺ Make a **tint** of a color, or lighten its value, by adding **white**.

☺ Make a **shade** of a color, or darken its value, by adding **black**.

ANIMAL SCIENCE

Q. What's the largest mammal?

a) Elephant

b) Blue Whale

c) Polar Bear

Student Save

Contestant Tim Maxwell answered: *Elephant*. Laura is good at Animal Science and saved Tim. Think before locking in your answer. A **mammal** is a warm-blooded animal that gives birth to its young. Bears have cubs. Elephants and whales have calves. Is a blue whale a fish or a mammal? It's bigger than the others!

An elephant is the largest land animal.

Polar bears are the largest of the bear species.

Q. Using the map, identify the continents.

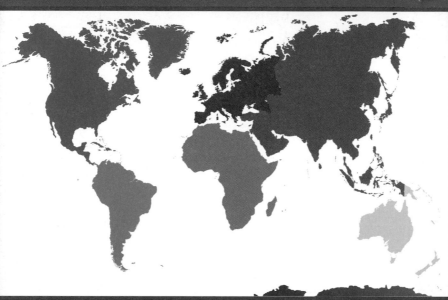

Spencer loves drawing pictures on his answer sheet. While he was waiting for your answer, he shaded in the continents ... but he didn't label them. Hey, you already used one cheat in this round!

Q. True or False? Five oceans form the World Ocean.

Flashback Hint

Contestant Avis Wrentmore walked away with $300,000 after she dropped out on this first-grade question:

What country is also a continent?

💡 (Hint: The answer will help you identify one continent: Australia. Now you just have to find it on the map.)

Brain Bubble

Out to Sea

Contestant Larry Rettig passed the first grade (see page 18), but was later shipwrecked by a question about the World Ocean's size. These facts would have kept him seaworthy:

☺ The World Ocean covers approximately 71% of the Earth.

☺ In 2000, the International Hydrographic Organization marked the boundaries of the "newest" ocean between 60 degrees south latitude and Antarctica.

Contestant Deborah Bassett knows all about the World Ocean. An environmentalist since age ten, she works for a nonprofit agency responsible for preserving the oceans, and plans on donating her tidal wave of $100,000 winnings to their ongoing conservation efforts.

Deborah & Spencer cheer for conservation!

Deborah Bassett

☺ PASS?

Larry Rettig sees his test scores.

DID YOU PASS OR FAIL?

Check your answers below. If you aced this part of the quiz, congratulations! You're smarter than a 1st grader! Move up to the 2nd grade. If you failed the quiz, you better spend more time studying!

☹ FAIL?

1ST GRADE ANSWERS:

Art: Red, blue, and yellow are primary colors.

Combinations for the secondary colors are: red + blue = purple; blue + yellow = green; red + yellow = orange.

Music: The banjo, bass, cello, dulcimer, harp, lute, and violin are all string instruments.

Hit, shake, or scratch a percussion instrument to make it vibrate and create music.

Animal Science: The blue whale (b) is a mammal and the largest in the world at an average 110 feet long and 210 tons. Its tongue is the size of an adult elephant.

World Geography: The seven continents are: Africa, Antarctica, Asia, Australia, Europe, North America, and South America.

True. The World Ocean is formed by five oceans: Arctic, Atlantic, Indian, Pacific, and Southern.

North America · Europe · Asia · Africa · South America · Australia · Antarctica

2ND GRADE

★ English

★ Health

★ Measurements

★ U.S. Presidents

Pick a student!

KYLE

Second grade isn't *exactly* a repeat of the first grade, but it feels familiar. You know the school, the basic subjects, and your classmates. Because study buddies are the way to go for tough tests, these contestants teamed up to make it through school. The first time that two family members split a desk was when Kelly Warren replaced husband Michael after he failed first grade. Kelly passed fourth grade and brought home the bacon with $175,000. A real double take came when identical twins shared quizzing duties. Are two brains smarter than one?

Husband and wife

The Warrens support each other!

ENGLISH

Q. Find the spelling mistakes in this sentence: "Every weak, we heard the tail of the fare knight and the bare until we whaled for the storyteller's reign to end."

Q. What is the suffix of the word "unfortunately"?

Q. What word that starts with the letter "Q" has a double meaning as a spike on a porcupine or a bird feather used as a pen?

Q. How many nouns are in the following sentence: "The twin brothers bought two motorcycles with their prize money."

Even with their amazing powers of "twin-tuition," brothers Chad and Cory Baumgartner made us blink and think twice, including themselves. Executive Producer Barry Poznick recounts, "The kids thought they were seeing double. We displayed a picture of them when they were one-year-olds, and the only person who could tell them apart was their mother in the audience. Even the twins didn't know who was who."

Chad and Cory Baumgartner twin up!

HEALTH

Q. Name two ball and socket joints in your body.

Q. True or False? The small intestine is longer than the large intestine.

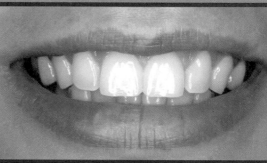

Q. Typical people have how many baby teeth as kids?
a) 20
b) 24
c) 28

Cheat COPY

Cheating in school isn't cool, but the adults on the show need help sometimes. Kyle saved contestant Tracy Baughman in 1st Grade Earth Science. Then he let her peek at his answer for 3rd Grade U.S. History. Tracy gave Laura a toothy smile after copying her correct answer for 2nd Grade Health . . . until she faced 2nd Grade Measurements minus saves and cheats. As Jeff calls it, "the kill-o-meter" [kilometer] did Tracy in, but she still won $25,000.

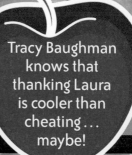

Tracy Baughman knows that thanking Laura is cooler than cheating . . . maybe!

21

MEASUREMENTS

Q. How many meters are in a kilometer?

Q. True or False? A millennium is 100 years.

Q. If March 1st falls on a Wednesday, on what day of the week does April 1st fall?

U.S. PRESIDENTS

Q. What man, who would later be President, was the Commander-in-Chief of the American army during the U.S. Revolutionary War?

Q. According to the U.S. Constitution, the President is part of which of the three branches of government?

Brain Bubble

You Make Cents

Contestant Ebony Graham danced her way through making change with this question: What is the minimum number of U.S. coins needed to make exactly 61 cents?

💡 Flashback Hint

She needed JFK, FDR, and Honest Abe. Ebony made it to 5th Grade Algebra before she ran out of presidential aid at $50,000.

Q. Match up the U.S. President with the U.S. currency featuring his face.

PRESIDENTS	CURRENCY
1) Thomas Jefferson	a) penny and $5
2) Andrew Jackson	b) nickel
3) George Washington	c) dime
4) Abraham Lincoln	d) quarter and $1
5) Franklin D. Roosevelt	e) half-dollar
6) Ulysses S. Grant	f) $20
7) John F. Kennedy	g) $50

Jeff and Kyle ask if you need their spare change.

☺ PASS?

DID YOU PASS OR FAIL?

Check your answers below. If you aced this part of the quiz, congratulations! You're smarter than a 2nd grader! Move up to the 3rd grade. If you failed the quiz, you should find a study buddy!

☹ FAIL?

Were two students smarter than five?

2ND GRADE ANSWERS:

English: There are five spelling mistakes: weak (week), tail (tale), fare (fair), bare (bear), and whaled (wailed).

The suffix of "unfortunately" is "ly." The prefix is "un," and the root is "fortunate."

Quill is a porcupine's needle and a writing instrument.

There are three nouns: brothers, motorcycles, and money.

Health: The human shoulders and hips are ball and socket joints.

True. The small intestine is about four times longer than the large intestine.

Kids typically have (a) 20 baby teeth.

Measurements: A kilometer equals 1,000 meters.

False. A millennium is 1,000 years; a century is 100 years.

April 1st would be a Saturday if March 1st were a Wednesday.

U.S. Presidents: George Washington.

The President is in the Executive branch, with Judicial and Legislative being the other two branches.

1b, 2f, 3d, 4a, 5c, 6g, 7e.

$3 \times 3 = 9$

3RD GRADE

- ★ Reading
- ★ Geometry
- ★ Earth Science
- ★ U.S. Geography

Pick a student!

SPENCER

Ask contestant Pat Germano how tough third grade is. You're beyond the basics and into the nitty-gritty details of book genres, many-sided shapes, cloud names, and state capitals. If contestants graduated in grade order to this level (rather than skipping between grades), then they have reached the golden halfway mark. Whether they fail or bail, the big kid pockets $25,000. Third grade is when contestants start second-guessing themselves or are too cool for school because they *know* the answers . . . or think they do.

A show-stopping moment!

Pat Germano made show history when he flunked out on his first question.

$6 \times 6 = 36$

Smarter Than a 5th Grader

READING

Q. Which of the following is *not* a book genre?

a) Fiction

b) Autobiography

c) Mystery

Q. True or False? Fiction books are not assigned numbers in the Dewey Decimal System.

Q. What is a book's summary?

Q. Match up the cause and its effect.

Cause	Effect
1. The spaceship landed.	a) Alana grabbed her kite.
2. The doorbell rang.	b) The dog ran away.
3. Jeff cooked BBQ.	c) The aliens invaded.
4. It was a windy day.	d) Spencer opened the door.
5. The dogcatcher drove by.	e) We ate dinner.

Brain Bubble

Shelved

Librarians and contestant Lakisha Livingston truly appreciate a man named Melvin Dewey. Before 1871, a comprehensive way to shelve books had not yet been invented. Librarians and readers were frustrated. Melvin, also a frustrated yet smart librarian, invented the Dewey Decimal System by assigning a number to a book's subject. Lakisha won $100,000 on her answer about his system before dropping out for more free reading time. Shelving tips for your next trip:

- ☺ 000 – 099 General
- ☺ 100 – 199 Philosophy and Psychology
- ☺ 200 – 299 Religion and Mythology
- ☺ 300 – 399 Social Science
- ☺ 400 – 499 Language
- ☺ 500 – 599 Math and Science
- ☺ 600 – 699 Medicine and Technology
- ☺ 700 – 799 Arts and Entertainment
- ☺ 800 – 899 Literature
- ☺ 900 – 999 History and Geography

GEOMETRY

Q. Which of the following is an octagon?

a)   b)   c)

Q. If you add a rhombus and a hexagon, what is the sum total of their sides?

Q. How many of the interior angles in a scalene triangle have the same number of degrees?

😮 Flunk Out

A student can't save a classmate with the same wrong answer. Contestant Crystal Robertson begged Alana for a save on this 3rd Grade Math stumper:

"A triangle has two interior angles of one degree each. How many degrees does its third angle have?"

Alana and Crystal both said, "One." They were wrong. Jacob wasn't at the podium and couldn't save Crystal with his correct answer: A triangle's total angles must equal 180 degrees, making the third angle 178 degrees. Crystal left without any allowance since she hadn't yet reached the halfway mark of $25,000.

EARTH SCIENCE

Q. True or False? Nimbus clouds are storm clouds.

Q. What is the lower layer of the Earth's atmosphere?
a) Mesosphere
b) Thermosphere
c) Troposphere

Q. In the southern hemisphere, the vernal equinox occurs in which month?

Q. Which of the following scales is used to measure earthquake intensity?
a) The Richter scale
b) The Saffir-Simpson scale
c) The Fujita scale

Brain Bubble

All Shook Up

The world we call home was a harsh subject for contestants. Contestant Roy Redulfin dropped out with $10,000 after 3rd Grade Earth Science shook his confidence. He wasn't sure which side of the equator was tilted left or right.

Contestant Pat Germano copied off Kyle on the atmospheric layers question. Kyle was wrong, and Pat's chances of winning any money evaporated into thin air.

Contestant Kelly Warren tipped the scales in her favor with her own correct answer about measuring natural forces and sailed into the 4th Grade.

💡 **Flashback Hint**

Two scales track wind speed, while one records the forceful shake of an earthquake.

7x7=49

U.S. GEOGRAPHY

Q. The following is an outline of what U.S. state?

HOST HINT

It's Jeff's home state.

★ Salem

Q. Salem is the capital of this state, which also has the world's smallest park at 452 square inches.

Q. The majority of Yellowstone National Park is located in what U.S. state?

Q. What state's main sport is dog mushing?

3RD GRADE

☺ PASS?

DID YOU PASS OR FAIL?

Check your answers below. If you aced this part of the quiz, congratulations! You're smarter than a 3rd grader! Move up to the 4th grade. If you failed the quiz, you should study more in study hall!

☹ FAIL?

ARE YOU SMARTER THAN A 5TH GRADER?

Spencer helps Sammy Traylor move on to the 4th grade!

3RD GRADE ANSWERS:

Reading: (a) Fiction is a book category, not a genre. Several genres, including Mystery, are filed under its listing. Autobiography genres are filed under the category of Nonfiction.

False. Fiction books are assigned numbers in the Dewey Decimal System.

A summary is a brief description of a book's story.

1c, 2d, 3e, 4a, 5b.

Geometry: (c) An eight-sided shape is an octagon.

A four-sided rhombus plus a six-sided hexagon equals a ten-sided decagon.

None. A scalene triangle has three unequal angles.

Earth Science: True. In Latin, *nimbus* means rain.

The troposphere (c) is the lowest layer of the Earth's atmosphere.

The vernal equinox starts on the first day of spring, and in the southern hemisphere springs starts in September.

(a) The Richter scale measures earthquake intensity. The Saffir-Simpson scale measures hurricane force. The Fujita scale measures tornado wind speed.

U.S. Geography: Georgia, Jeff's home state.

Salem is the capital of Oregon, which also has a snail-racing park in the city of Portland.

Yellowstone spans three states: 1% located in Idaho; 3% in Montana; 96% in Wyoming.

Alaska.

7x7=49

AaBbCcDdEe

4TH GRADE

- ★ Math
- ★ Physical Sciences
- ★ Social Studies
- ★ World History

Pick a student!

Entering fourth grade is a life-changing time. You've made your mark, established yourself in the school community, formed opinions and interests in specific subjects, and now you're spreading your wings. Explore different cultures in Social Studies and their impact in World History. Flip fractions in Math. Settle in for elemental studies in Physical Sciences. Answers open up new avenues to pursue. Contestant Sammy Traylor seized his moment during 4th Grade Math and made show history.

A life-changing answer for Sammy Traylor!

MATH

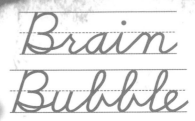

Q. What is the reciprocal of ¾?

Q. In square inches, what is ½ of the area of a square with 12-inch sides?

Q. What is the sum of 11.5 and -14?

Q. What is the numeric value of the Roman numerals "LXV"?

1 2 3 4 5
6 7 8 9

Brain Bubble

Count on It!

Math always divides and conquers the class, especially the higher grades. The very first contestant on the show, Seth Finn, skipped grades in search of a good monetary sum. He totaled $5,000 after copying a correct answer off Spencer about square inches.

Copying doesn't guarantee correct answers. Remember Tim Maxwell from the 1st grade, the contestant saved by Laura? Tim made it beyond the halfway mark into 4th Grade Math when he copied Spencer's answer about supplementary angles. Unfortunately, Spencer was wrong by 100 degrees. Tim flunked out with $25,000.

But contestant John Zoll graduated into the big-money category using his unique method of handling positive and negative numbers. Jeff laughed, "That was the most bizarre display of elementary school math I've ever seen. It was funky math!"

The biggest answer came in a history-making moment by contestant Sammy Traylor. He didn't know the 4th Grade Math brain buster, but he knew the answer he wanted from girlfriend Marsha Pollashaff. Sammy won $50,000 and, before admitting he wasn't smarter than those fifth graders, he asked Marsha to marry him. She knew the answer to his question: YES!

PHYSICAL SCIENCES

Q. What is the term for the study of dinosaurs?

Q. What era did the earliest humans first appear?
   a) Paleozoic
   b) Mesozoic
   c) Cenozoic

Q. On the Periodic Table of Elements, what are the letters used for a vitamin found in milk?

Q. Using the atom graphic below, locate the proton, electron, and neutron.

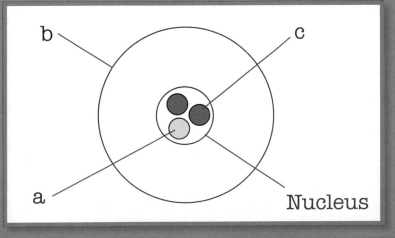

SOCIAL STUDIES

Q. What is the name for the form of picture writing used by the ancient Egyptians?

Q. Which culture's renewed interest in the arts and learning established the Renaissance?

Q. Name the Western explorer who shared the ways of many cultures with the Grand Khan Kublai?

Q. True or False? The Nobel Peace Prize is awarded every year in Stockholm, Sweden.

Memorable Moment

Twin contestants, Chad and Cory Baumgartner, gambled on Jacob's smarts in saving them twice in different categories. Jacob is a strong student in many subjects, including Geography (a save) and Social Studies (a copy). He helped the twins rack up $175,000 in winnings and make it through fourth grade. The brothers dropped out when faced by a fifth-grade question about the Nobel Peace Prize. Too bad they hadn't read our Brain Bubble (see next page) before taking the quiz!

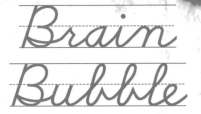

Peaceful Prizewinners

Here's some background on the most inspirational, and controversial, worldwide honor: the Nobel Peace Prize.

In his will, Swedish inventor and industrialist Alfred Nobel left 94% of his life savings for the establishment of five awards given annually to individuals whose out-standing work in various subjects benefited mankind.

In 1901, the first five Nobel Awards were given for Physics, Chemistry, Literature, Physiology or Medicine, and Peace. A sixth category, Economics, was established in his memory by Sweden's central bank in 1968.

Nobel created the peace category out of concern for the misuse of his own work — perfecting the explosive, dynamite — for destructive rather than positive goals.

Q. Which nations were at war during the Hundred Years' War?

Q. Which explorer sailed around the globe in 1522?

Q. What is one reason for the Irish emigration to America in the 19th century?

Q. True or False? NATO stands for "North Atlantic Treaty Organization."

☺ PASS?

Jacob is so nice to save the twins twice!

Stephanie Wambach aced the 4th grade!

DID YOU PASS OR FAIL?

Check your answers below. If you aced this part of the quiz, congratulations! You're smarter than a 4th grader! Move up to the 5th grade. If you failed the quiz, it's time to knuckle down, buckle down, and study, study, study before asking for a "do-over."

☹ FAIL?

4TH GRADE ANSWERS:

Math: To get the reciprocal of a fraction, you flip the top with the bottom: $\frac{4}{3}$

Use this formula: Length x Width = Area. $12 \times 12 = 144 \div 2 = 72$.

$11.5 + -14 = -2.5$

Roman numeral "LXV" is $60 + 5 = 65$.

Physical Sciences: Paleontology is the study of prehistoric life, including dinosaurs. The Greek root words form the term: *paleo* is "ancient," *ontos* is "being," and *logos* is "knowledge."

Early humans first appeared in the (c) Cenozoic era, which is also the name of the current time period.

"Ca" represents Calcium.

(a) proton, (b) electron, (c) neutron

Social Studies: Hieroglyphics.

The Renaissance, an age of cultural enlightenment, was ignited by artists and philosophers of Florence, Italy.

Marco Polo, a Venetian, became Kublai Khan's diplomat for 17 years.

False. The Nobel Peace Prize is awarded in Oslo, Norway, while the other prizes are awarded in Stockholm, Sweden.

World History: England and France fought from 1337 – 1453 for control of France.

Ferdinand Magellan.

Potato crop failures in 1846 caused famine among the Irish.

True.

5TH GRADE

★ **Astronomy**

★ **Algebra**

★ **U.S. History**

★ **Literature**

Pick a student!

ALANA

You've made it into fifth grade. You've mastered the basics and conquered the complex subjects. You're a certified smarty-pants in our TV classroom. The future is filled with promise. But do you have the right stuff to blast off into the scholarly stratosphere? Our contestants are shiny with perspiration and anticipation of a chance at half-a-million dollars. Some just drop out. Others show that their school smarts still sparkle after all those years spent playing grown-up.

Steve Nalepa teaches "the worm" to Jeff and Alana.

ASTRONOMY

Q. Name the 17th century scientist who is considered the "father of modern astronomy."

Q. The planet Mars has how many moons?

Q. In the initials of the federal agency known as NASA, what word does the first "A" stand for?

Cheat PEEK

Peeking at someone's paper doesn't mean they've got the right answer. Will you go with their answer or one of your own? Contestant Steve Nalepa didn't peek for the NASA question. Jeff peeked at the papers. Spencer said, "American." Jacob said, "Alliance." Jeff said, "Aerospace." Steve stuck with his own answer and passed fifth grade.

Steve Nalepa gets an "A" for effort.

ALGEBRA

Q. If y = 3x and 3x = 12, then what number does "y" equal?

Q. In this formula, 2x + y = 24, y = 8. What does "x" equal?

Q. A meter is 39 inches. How many feet is 3 meters?

U.S. HISTORY

Q. What man, who would later be U.S. President, represented the British soldiers who were on trial for the Boston massacre?

Q. In what year did explorers Lewis and Clark complete their expedition across the American West?
   a) 1804
   b) 1805
   c) 1806

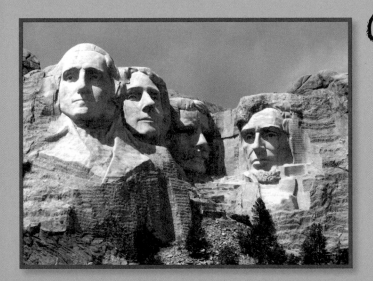

Q. Name the father and son sculptors who carved the portraits of four U.S. Presidents into Mount Rushmore.

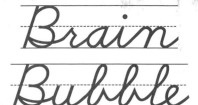

Brain Bubble

The Adams Family

Contestant "Jumping John" Zoll fell down in relief after agonizing over the answer about the lawyer who became President. Was it John Adams or John Quincy Adams? Classmate Alana wrote, "James Madison." She was wrong and John, the contestant, was right about the President named John. Do you know the differences between the families Adams? They were the first father-and-son Commanders-in-Chief.

John Adams
- ☺ Second U.S. President
- ☺ Term 1797 – 1801
- ☺ First Vice President

John Quincy Adams
- ☺ Sixth U.S. President
- ☺ Term 1825 – 1829
- ☺ First President to have his photo taken

Q. A pseudonym is an alias, or fake name, used by writers. Which name below is a pseudonym?
a) Samuel Clemens
b) Lewis Carroll
c) Charles Dickens

Q. Define the role of the antagonist in a story.

Q. True or False? A memoir is a collection of award-winning short stories.

☺ PASS?

DID YOU PASS OR FAIL?

Check your answers below. If you aced this part of the quiz, congratulations! You *might* be smarter than a 5th grader! But did you study enough for our final exam? If you failed the quiz, ask a friend to help you fine-tune your school skills. The more you practice, the better you'll be. Just ask the top students of this season.

☹ FAIL?

John Zoll may need the school nurse.

5TH GRADE ANSWERS:

Astronomy: Galileo Galilei (1564 – 1642) was an astronomer whose experiments propelled the scientific revolution.

The planet Mars has two moons, Phobos and Deimos.

NASA is the abbreviation for the National Aeronautics and Space Administration.

Algebra: y = 12.

24 − 8 = 16 ÷ 2 = 8, so x = 8.

The equation 3 x 39 ÷ 12 = 9 feet 9 inches.

U.S. History: John Adams.

(c) Meriwether Lewis and William Clark began their expedition on May 14, 1804, and completed it on September 23, 1806.

Sculptors Gutzon and Lincoln Borglum carved the 60-foot-tall portraits of George Washington, Thomas Jefferson, Theodore Roosevelt, and Abraham Lincoln from 1927 to 1941.

Literature: Charles Lutwidge Dodgson was known as (b) Lewis Carroll for his most famous work in the genre of literary nonsense, *Alice's Adventures in Wonderland*. Samuel Clemens wrote as "Mark Twain" and Charles Dickens wrote as "Boz."

The antagonist tries to block the hero, or protagonist, from achieving his or her goals.

False. A memoir is a nonfiction collection of personal essays, letters, or articles about a historical event or person's life.

MILLION-DOLLAR QUESTIONS

- ★ U.S. History
- ★ Math ★ Astronomy
- ★ Music
- ★ Health

Special student tutor!

MARKI

On the show, the final exam is worth one million dollars. A contestant, having completed first through fifth grades and earned $500,000, chooses to answer the final question. They risk losing their winnings down to $25,000 and must admit they weren't smart enough to complete the quiz. These six contestants reached this stage: Alex Outhred, John Zoll, Steve Nalepa, Stephanie Wambach, Robert Rutter, and Victor King. Unlike them, you have Marki as your special tutor. She won't help you cheat, but she'll give you some hints. How high will your test score be?

John Zoll and Marki reach for scholarly heights!

U.S. HISTORY

Q. Who was the first U.S. Secretary of the Treasury?

Tutor Time

The Treasury printed money. Maybe the first secretary likes seeing his face.

John Zoll made the show fun for everyone.

MATH

Q. What is the only prime number that is a factor of 16?

Tutor Time

Prime numbers are divided by themselves and 1, with 0 remainders.

TALLY UP

Alex and Stephanie were the only contestants to know the right answer to the million-dollar question, but they had chosen not to answer it and instead, dropped out with $500,000. So did Victor and John, who broke down in tears of relief after dropping out because he had no clue to his question's answer. Steve took on the one-million-dollar question and answered that *Mercury* was the first U.S. satellite launched into space in 1962. He was wrong, and flunked out with $25,000.

ASTRONOMY

Q. What was the name of the first satellite put into orbit by the United States?

Stephanie Wambach knew the right answer!

Tutor Time

Satellites launched into space didn't always need an astronaut onboard.

MUSIC

Q. In the 1720s, what man composed a series of violin concertos known as "The Four Seasons"?

Tutor Time

This Venetian violinist captured nature's vibrancy in his concertos.

Victor King drops out!

HEALTH

Q. Of the 32 teeth in the typical adult human mouth, how many are bicuspids?

Tutor Time

Bicuspids are paired up in the mouth's corners.

Check your answers below. If you aced the final exam, you ARE smarter than any of this season's contestants. Congratulations! If you failed the final exam, don't give up! Life and school are all about learning from your answers, right and wrong. Go study some more and you'll improve your score the next time around.

School's over for Steve Nalepa!

MILLION-DOLLAR ANSWERS:

U.S. History: Alexander Hamilton, featured on the $10 bill, was the first Secretary of the U.S. Treasury.

Math: 2 is the only prime number that is a factor of 16.

Astronomy: *Explorer* was the first unmanned satellite launched by the United States in 1958.

Music: Composer and violinist Antonio Lucio Vivaldi (1678 – 1741) wrote the popular violin concertos, "The Four Seasons."

Health: There are eight bicuspids in the typical adult human mouth, with two pairs in each quadrant.

CLASS DISMISSED

There were many memorable show moments this year. Steve Nalepa had the most: He went the furthest in the quiz without using any cheats; was the first to try the one-million-dollar question; and experience the largest drop in winnings of $475,000. This Yale graduate was *almost* smarter than his classmates in test-taking. Each of these top students knew the golden rule: Enjoy life, whatever your age. A member of a break-dancing crew during his school days, Steve showed off his moves whenever he aced a grade. The best contestants have fun while learning at their desks. Now it's your turn to make school and life fun for you!

Steve Nalepa "breaks" onstage!

MEMORY LANE